A Basic Guide to Technopathic Stress
© 2015 Grahame Gardner
Published by Western Geomancy
Glasgow G11 5HD
http://westerngeomancy.org
westerngeomancy@gmail.com

Graphics by Arla Kean
http://www.akeandesign.co.uk/

Printed by Glasgow Cross Press
http://www.glasgowcrosspress.com

First published May 2015
Second edition January 2016

ISBN 978-0-9932347-2-9

A
Basic Guide
to

Technopathic Stress

Grahame Gardner

Acknowledgements

Grateful thanks to Roy Riggs who started the whole thing, Ros Briagha of The Geomancy Group who originally coined the term 'technopathic stress', Dr Patrick MacManaway for proofreading and foreword, Dai Vaughan and Susan Collins for helpful advice on the practicalities of self-publishing, Arla for her wonderful graphics, Jill Moss for additional proofreading and overall encouragement, and of course Elspeth for putting up with me.

By the same author:

Dowsing Magic – from Water Finds to Dragon Lines
Published by Penwith Press ISBN 978-0-9533316-5-9

Contents

Foreword

Plato declared the Gods to be numbers – each archetypal energy having its own particular frequency and wave-form, perceived by the human senses as vibrations in the ether.

Our modern term for Plato's ether is the electro-magnetic field within which we live, surrounded as we are by the dancing, ever shifting tides in the geo-magnetosphere, played into resonance by the drumming of the solar wind and the long slow music of the spheres.

We ourselves are electromagnetic beings, living within our own mini-magnetosphere generated by the spark of our heart-beat, holding within that resonant space all the frequencies of our thoughts and feelings, our metabolism and physiology.

The range of frequencies at work in human physiology covers a wide range of the electromagnetic spectrum, and we have evolved naturally adapted to the environmental input of the resonance surrounding us.

By changing our external electromagnetic environment, we change by response and reaction our own internal electromagnetic environment, with either beneficial, neutral or detrimental result, depending on the frequency and wave-form perceived.

Health concerns over detrimental effects are currently matters of discussion, debate and ongoing research.

Disturbances of mood and sleep cycles are common due to electromagnetic influence on the pineal gland, and low grade adrenal stimulation generating chronic stress are well recognized, as are a myriad of other interconnected and independent effects on our complex biological systems.

Increasing public awareness of these potential hazards has led to a widespread desire and need to understand these issues clearly, and to be advised and guided in a straightforward way that allows us to navigate with awareness and sensibility in our contemporary technological environment.

In the pages that follow, Grahame has given us exactly that information and guidance, with both clarity and simplicity as well as necessary technical detail.

I both congratulate and thank him on behalf of those of us for whom technology starts and ends with a light switch.

Dr Patrick MacManaway

Introduction

This 'Guide to Technopathic Stress' started life as a short photocopied leaflet that I drew up to give out to my clients so that they had something to study at their leisure instead of trying to remember what I had told them during a consultation. Over time, it has gradually grown larger until it has developed into the form you see today. It has by no means finished evolving, as new sources of technopathic stress are emerging daily in our modern gadget-hungry Western society and increasing numbers of people are finding themselves to be suffering from electro hyper-sensitivity – or EHS for short.

This 'book' version first appeared in 2015, and is constantly being revised and updated. The availability of 'on-demand' printing has made it viable to produce in short print runs so that editions can be kept up to date without having too much of an outlay on printed copies. It is also available as an e-book.

What's new in the Second Edition

This edition contains several revisions and updated research, together with additional material on airport scanners, wind turbines and ground currents. I omitted these from the first edition as the hazards are comparatively extremely low; however many people have asked me about them since then, so it feels appropriate to include them for completeness.

How to use this book

Please note that this is not intended to be a scientific document and indeed is deliberately kept simple to avoid overloading the text with too much data and references.

The book is designed to function as a quick reference guide that you can dip into anywhere as needed. Each chapter deals with a different hazard, listing the likely effects of over-exposure and some methods that can be employed to manage your exposure to that particular radiation.

The chapters are listed in decreasing order of severity - so for the hazards listed at the beginning of the book, many people will notice effects; whereas for those towards the end of the book only a few highly sensitive people are likely to notice effects. You can think of it as a 'risk assessment' for the home, school and office environment.

Scientific data is available via the books and websites listed at the end if you want to research things further, and I would strongly encourage you to inform yourself by doing so.

What is
Technopathic Stress?

What is Technopathic Stress?

Technopathic stress is a fairly new phenomenon that has only arisen in the last 20 years or so as a result of our addictive love affair with gadgets and technology. To support this obsession, phone masts and microwave transmitters now cover our countryside blighting some of our most beautiful scenery, many large cities have public Wi-Fi networks, an average of 75% of the world's population now own a mobile phone (over 90% in the USA), and it is rare to find a home that does not contain several wireless devices like tablets, games consoles, surround sound systems and so on.

We are living in a complex and unprecedented soup of electromagnetic radiation and we are all taking part in a global experiment whether we like it or not. Life on planet Earth has evolved in harmony with the background geomagnetic field generated by the planet and many of our bodily cycles are dependent on this. Over the last hundred or so years we have been exposed to modulated radio-frequency (RF) fields since the development of radio and television transmissions, but nothing in our history has prepared us for the explosive increase in pulsed microwave radiation from our phones and other communication devices that we are now being subjected to, and we still have little idea of how this will affect us in the long-term. Government safety levels for exposure to electromagnetic fields (EMFs) are by and large based on research that was done back in the 1960s, and the technology has evolved too rapidly for the bureaucracy to keep up.

Broadly speaking, the main culprits can be divided into digital pulsed radio-frequency fields from mobile phone masts, cordless phones in the home, Wi-Fi networks and other microwave-based technologies; and power-frequency fields from transformers, power lines, mains wiring and electrical appliances in the home etc. Another factor to consider is 'dirty electricity', a name given to higher-frequency interference from various sources that is carried on the domestic mains wiring.

Although more sceptical researchers claim that any perceived detrimental effects are purely psychological in nature, a growing number of scientific studies, particularly from European investigators, suggest that prolonged exposure to these various radiations can affect the immune system and cause serious health problems. More and more people are finding themselves suffering from electro hyper-sensitivity.

Because of the relative newness of the phenomenon, long-term research is still lacking. However, many countries and organisations in Europe and elsewhere have recommended or already adopted much lower levels of exposure than the UK; for example the public health department of Salzburg has advised against wireless networks and DECT phones being installed in schools and nurseries, and the German teachers' union has instructed its members to resist installation of school Wi-Fi on safety grounds. In Canada, Lakehead University in Ontario opted to restrict the use of wireless to certain limited areas as they consider the technology to be unproven and therefore not safe,[1] and in February 2015, France passed a law banning Wi-Fi use in pre-schools and other facilities catering to children under 3 years of age and instructed other schools that Wi-Fi must be disabled when not required for lessons.[2] Also in February 2015, Lloyd's of London introduced a general exclusion clause that specifically excludes claims *"...directly or indirectly arising out of, resulting from or contributed to by electromagnetic fields, electromagnetic radiation, electromagnetism, radio waves or noise.*" [3]

In 2011 the World Health Organisation and International Agency for Research on Cancer (IARC) classified RF electromagnetic fields as 'Class (2B): possibly carcinogenic to humans, based on an increased risk of glioma, a malignant type of brain cancer associated with wireless phone use'.[4]

What are the symptoms?

Most EHS sufferers will notice symptoms that vary depending on their location and will usually be less severe or disappear completely in rural environments. Typical early symptoms include insomnia, poor sleep, unexplained headaches, sinus congestion, memory loss and difficulty concentrating or thinking clearly. More severe cases can involve skin rashes, ME, irritability, neuralgia, nosebleeds, tinnitus and light sensitivity – possibly even MS.[5] The effects are cumulative if unchecked and some extreme sufferers have been forced to give up their jobs and homes and live in rural environments free from technological influences.

People with amalgam dental fillings or metal implants tend to be more susceptible to EHS. Such people may find that undergoing a process of heavy metal detoxification will help alleviate the symptoms, as will replacement of the fillings.

The science bit

All energy, and thus by extension all matter in the Universe, has a frequency of vibration and is part of the electromagnetic spectrum. Humans can perceive only the very tiny slice of the spectrum that is visible light, which has a frequency range around 10^{15}Hz (Hertz=cycles per second). Surrounding the small window of visible light are the bands of infrared light, which has a lower frequency extending down to around 10^{13}Hz, and ultraviolet light, which has a higher frequency extending up to just above 10^{16}Hz. We know from exposure to the sun that the higher frequencies of ultraviolet cause skin burns and ultimately melanomas, and this defines the lower boundary of the ionising radiation part of the spectrum.[6]

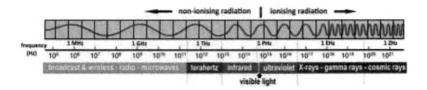

As the frequency gets higher the wavelength gets smaller and smaller, and the radiation is more penetrating and likely to cause genetic damage. Here we find X-rays, gamma rays and cosmic rays. Conversely, as the frequency gets lower below infrared the wavelength becomes longer (above 1mm) and we move into the region referred to as non-ionising radiation, inhabited by the microwaves used in our phones, Wi-Fi and microwave ovens, and lower still the broadcast and wireless bands used by television and radio.

Sandwiched between the microwaves and infrared parts of the spectrum is a band known as 'sub-millimetre', 'terahertz' (1THz=10^{12} Hz), or sometimes 'far-infrared'. Everything that emits heat emits this radiation, and that includes you and me. Because terahertz radiation is easily absorbed by water (e.g. in

9

the Earth's atmosphere), this band remains largely unexploited for terrestrial communications as it is difficult to transmit over long distances, but it is important to astronomers who can detect terahertz radiation emitted by astronomical bodies and many powerful high-altitude and space-borne radio telescopes operate in this band. It is also finding uses in low-penetration medical screening techniques and airport scanners as the waves can easily penetrate clothing (more on this in Chapter 13). The higher frequency range of terahertz radiation means that if the technical difficulties can be overcome it could provide dramatically greater communications bandwidth, enabling short-range broadband connections that are around 100 times faster than existing Wi-Fi speeds. We are likely to see terahertz devices replacing or supplementing internal domestic and business Wi-Fi systems within the next few years.

An even more exciting development is 'Li-Fi', which uses visible light frequencies to transmit data through LED lighting systems. This was invented by Professor Harald Haas at Edinburgh University back in 2011, and astonishing speeds of 224 gigabits per second have recently been demonstrated.[7] The Li-Fi signal uses light frequencies between 400 and 800 terahertz, pulsing the light on and off at frequencies too fast for the eye to notice, and it can even be used when the light is effectively 'off' as far as human vision is concerned. The technology is still being developed, but it looks set to become a safer, faster and more secure short-range alternative to Wi-Fi in the not-too-distant future. You can imagine a shopping mall or factory floor where every light fitting becomes a super-fast broadband transmitter. Whether the Li-Fi high-frequency pulsing has any physiological or psychological effect on us remains to be seen, but it certainly looks like a very promising safer alternative to microwave-based Wi-Fi.

Just because the microwave frequencies are classed as 'non-ionising' does not mean that they have no effect on the body. At sufficiently high power levels, any RF radiation, particularly those in the microwave frequency range, will have a heating effect on living tissue. The accepted exposure levels for microwave radiation are based on the thermal effects it has on body cells – i.e. the level at which the water molecules in the body start to heat up, just as your microwave oven heats food. The research that set these levels was conducted back in the 1960s when microwave ovens were first introduced, and that in turn was based on observations by technicians developing the new technology of radar during the Second World War, when they noticed that they could warm their hands up on cold winter days by placing them in the beams of their magnetron devices. Percy Spencer, an American engineer working for Raytheon, noticed that a chocolate bar in his pocket was melted by the microwave radiation, and went on to produce a working prototype of a microwave oven by the simple expedient of connecting the output of the magnetron to a metal box where the microwaves could not escape.[8] As many of the early radar technicians went on to develop various forms of cancer, including leukaemia, non-Hodgkin's lymphoma, breast or testicular cancer and melanoma, it quickly became clear that at high levels these microwave radiations were detrimental to humans. Consequently, the recommended exposure limits are set far below these thermal levels, based on an 'average' power density. At these 'non-thermal' levels, it is claimed that there is no biological effect on the body. However, the pulsed microwave signals used in modern digital communications have peak pulses many times higher than these average levels and are modulated several times a second (DECT cordless phones can have peak levels 100 times higher than their 'average' level). There is growing evidence demonstrating that biological effects still occur at these levels. In simple terms, cell membranes in the body are over-stimulated (stressed), which disrupts their natural cycle of nutrient absorption and toxin elimination.

One of the most prolific researchers on the subject is Dr Andrew Goldsworthy of Imperial College London, who says: "Cell membranes in the body are electrically charged and the pulsed radio waves used by mobiles make them vibrate, dislodging the calcium that binds the cells together. This makes them more permeable and releases enzymes that can damage the DNA in genes, including those that protect against cancer."[9] This genetic damage to DNA is irreversible and may be responsible for birth defects and genetic disorders like autism. The incidence of autism has increased exponentially in the last 20 years, and some researchers like Dr Martha Herbert of the Harvard Medical School have linked this to the rise in environmental exposure to EMFs.[10]

Recognition of possible detrimental effects from non-thermal levels of radiation varies from country to country. Russia accepted that ill health could result from non-thermal levels as far back as 1958 when it set much lower safety limits than the UK. It is well documented that the US Embassy in Moscow suffered intense microwave bombardment by the Soviets from 1953 to 1976; however at the time the US refused to accept that any detrimental effects transpired from this, largely because the detected levels were far below their own defined exposure standards and to admit to any effects would have resulted in a profusion of domestic claims. Consequently, it wasn't until 1986 that the National Academy of Sciences' NRC accepted non-thermal effects from microwave radiation. The UK's current protocols were set in 1996 and do not take into account *any* non-thermal effects. Many organisations, such as the International Commission for Electromagnetic Safety, the EU Environmental Agency, the EU Parliament, and the Council of Europe, regard the UK's 'heating' limits as obsolete and call for non-thermal limits to be adopted in the UK. Denis Henshaw, emeritus professor of Human Radiation Effects at Bristol University, says that the UK government is "poorly advised".[11]

A report issued in March 2015 of a well-conducted replication study conclusively demonstrated that long-term moderate levels of exposure to modulated RF fields can act as a co-carcinogen (i.e. actively promotes tumour growth). The levels tested were around 50 times lower than the currently recommended UK exposure levels.[12] Even insects are affected by EMFs – there is a famous video produced by Dr John Ott showing a group of aphids on a leaf 'twitching' in time with the sweep from a radar facility 14 miles away.[13]

At a psychological level, the pulse frequencies of the signals used in phone and Wi-Fi communications are in some cases very close to our natural brainwave frequencies, and this can 'entrain' our brain waves into unnatural rhythms, causing sleeplessness, depression and other psychological problems. Tests have been conducted with blindfolded subjects that consistently provoked neurological symptoms with pulsed frequencies, while exposure to continuous frequencies did not.[14] I have certainly observed myself that I have trouble sleeping in the presence of Wi-Fi and DECT telephones, which is what started me researching the subject.

> I was staying in a bed & breakfast in Dublin for three nights and did not manage to sleep at all during that time, although the bed was very comfortable and the room was warm and quiet. On my departure, I discovered that the room was directly above the reception desk, who had their Wi-Fi router on the ceiling right below where my bed was located.
>
> In a few other places that I have stayed in for several nights at a time, I have requested that the Wi-Fi be switched off at night to ensure a good night's sleep. On the few instances where I did not sleep, it always transpired that they had forgotten to switch if off on those nights.
>
> Simple steps like switching off your Wi-Fi at night can have a powerful effect on your EMF exposure, and that's the main aim behind this little book.

The effects of power frequency EMFs have been better documented as we have lived with them for longer. Few would deny that there is a connection between high voltage power lines and childhood leukaemia, just as we now know that over-exposure to ultraviolet radiation causes skin cancer. There has been less documentation on the electric and magnetic fields emitted by many domestic appliances, and the effect these have on electro-sensitive individuals. Several of my clients had ailments that could be directly attributed to proximity to electricity meters or appliances and found relief from their symptoms once the cause was established and removed from the sleeping area. More on this in Chapter Nine.

'Dirty Electricity' (DE) is the name given to higher-frequency RF interference overtones or 'noise' that is carried on mains wiring installations. It is produced by many appliances such as fridge motors, computers, televisions, dimmer switches, fluorescent lights and other electronic devices that have a switched mode power supply and you may notice it in the form of brief bursts of interference on your television picture. The majority of it is usually generated by appliances inside the home, but some can be carried into the home from external sources on the incoming mains cable; this is particularly likely in apartment blocks sharing a common mains supply. The frequency range occupied by DE lies between that of power frequency EMFs and the high radio frequency microwaves of Wi-Fi, mobiles and DECT cordless phones and is often referred to as 'Intermediate Frequency' or 'IF'. With the increasing proliferation of electronic gadgetry in the home, dirty electricity is becoming more of a problem for very sensitive EHS sufferers. We'll cover this in Chapter Twelve.

What can we do?

It is still possible to maintain a technological lifestyle by following some basic steps, as outlined herein. In particular, it is important to minimise your exposure to technopathic influences in the bedroom, as this is where you are likely to spend the most time when at home, and it is during sleep that the immune system repairs itself. It is when the body is deprived of the natural sleep that it needs that the immune system becomes compromised and over time we become ill.

DECT Cordless Phones

DECT Cordless Phones

The acronym DECT stands for Digital Enhanced Cordless Telecommunications, and is the standard developed in Europe for cordless telephone systems, replacing the earlier analogue systems. It is also used in Australia and most countries in Asia and South America. The United States uses a similar system usually known as DECT 6.0, but this operates in a different frequency range so the two are not compatible. DECT devices are most commonly found in home cordless telephones, but the technology is utilised in other applications like intercom systems, office phone networks, baby monitors and industrial remote control devices. It is also sometimes used in traffic lights, cash terminals, and even remote-controlled door openers.

There is a low-power variant called DECT ULE (Ultra Low Energy) that can be used in battery-powered devices. This is becoming popular in home automation and security systems where the devices can be controlled by a smartphone application.

Frequency range: 1800 – 1930 MHz, also now some in the 2.4GHz and 5.6GHz bands, depending on country. DECT ULE operates in the 1.9GHz range. Because the frequency bands used vary between countries, it is not possible to use European DECT devices in the USA (or vice versa) as this will cause interference with other devices.

Average transmission power: 10mW (250mW peak) in Europe, 4mW (100mW peak) in US.

Hazards

DECT base stations transmit high levels of pulsed microwave radiation all the time, even when not in use, unlike the older analogue systems that only transmitted when a call was in progress. The relative power density this produces in the home is higher than if you had a phone mast at the bottom of your garden. This constitutes *chronic exposure*.

When in use, the power levels of the handset are similar or higher to those generated by a mobile phone, with the same associated risks. A DECT phone has an average output power of 10mW, but the signal is pulsed 100 times a second at peaks up to 250mW, whereas most mobiles peak at 225mW or lower, and this signal is transmitting *all the time*. This is the main reason that DECT phones are categorised in this book as more hazardous than cell phones.

Many DECT systems are not as secure as they should be, allowing interception and possible decryption of call information by hackers. Of course this is a problem with analogue systems too and is unlikely to be a concern for most people, but business users should be aware that using a DECT phone does not in itself guarantee secure communications.

Solutions

If at all possible use normal wired landline phones. These do not emit any radiation whatsoever, the call quality is much better, and they will never drop the call because of signal loss.

If you simply must have a cordless phone, use a 'low radiation' model such as one from the German-made Gigaset range. In Europe these are widely available in several models and they have their own integral encryption so are more secure than some other DECT phones. They incorporate an 'ECO-DECT' mode, whereby the base station goes into a power-saving state and emits zero radiation when not making or receiving calls. Although some other manufacturers claim similar features, most only reduce their power output and still transmit some radiation when on standby. To my knowledge, only the Gigaset range has the capacity to completely shut down when the phone is not in use. You can enable this from the handset settings menu (look for 'ECO-DECT' or 'ECO-DECT PLUS').
See: http://www.gigaset.com

In North America, there used to be a similar low-radiation phone called the Vtech 5.8. This is no longer manufactured, but you may be able to find one second-hand. The current Vtech 6.0 models do include ECO-DECT features, but so far I have been unable to determine whether this means that they shut down completely when not in use (as the 5.8 model did), or simply reduce the power to a lower level as some other models do.

Be aware that some other less scrupulous manufacturers claim to be 'eco-friendly' but this may only refer to the fact that the packaging material is recycled!

Warning: Research has shown that using a cordless DECT phone carries the same or greater risk of developing a malignant brain tumour as using a mobile phone.[15] If you are a heavy phone user (perhaps through work) you should definitely stick to using a wired landline phone.

At my home apartment, a downstairs neighbour purchased a new DECT cordless phone and installed the base station on her bedside table and the extension outlet in her kitchen, which was directly underneath my own bed position.

After puzzling over my lack of sleep for some weeks after she had moved in, I switched on my microwave test meter and found that there was a hot-spot of DECT radiation directly over my pillow.

The neighbour was understandably somewhat taken aback when I knocked on her door and asked to talk to her about the cordless phone in her bedroom, but when I explained the situation she agreed that she hadn't been sleeping well either since she'd moved in.

As a flat-warming present I bought her a low-radiation Gigaset ECO-DECT phone to replace her existing one, and we all sleep a lot better now.

Wireless Internet (Wi-Fi)

Wireless networks (Wi-Fi)

Wi-Fi, also WLAN, Wi-Max, is a protocol for providing wireless local area networks (hence WLAN) for data transmission. It is becoming near-ubiquitous both indoors and out, with many home-use devices requiring Wi-Fi capability, shops, trains and cafes providing free Wi-Fi for customers, and many towns and cities now offering access to public Wi-Fi networks in outdoor areas.

Wi-Fi is used most commonly by laptop computers, tablets and smartphones, but you also find devices like games consoles, smart televisions and other domestic appliances with Wi-Fi capability. Some games consoles (e.g. the X-Box) actually transmit Wi-Fi all the time, even when switched off, unless you physically unplug them from the mains power supply. Nowadays with the increasing advance of the 'internet of things' you find Wi-Fi built into many domestic appliances, such as television repeaters (e.g. Slingbox), wireless loudspeaker systems, cordless headphones – you can even buy colour-changing LED light bulbs that can be programmed from your smartphone.

Wi-Fi is a very adaptable technology because the protocol allows for the signal to frequency-hop to different bands, which helps reduce interference and signal drop-outs. Interestingly, this idea of frequency-hopping was first patented by the actress Hedy Lamarr (in conjunction with George Antheil) as early as 1942, as a method for preventing signals to radio-controlled torpedoes being jammed by enemy ships. Sadly, due to opposition from the US Navy it was not implemented during the war and was finally utilised by US military in 1962, after the patent had expired. Lamarr was finally honoured in 1997 when the Electronic Frontier

Foundation gave her an extremely belated award in recognition of her services.[16]

Hazards

Wi-Fi networks and other devices operate in a similar frequency range and cause similar problems as DECT cordless phones. Wi-Fi power levels fluctuate depending on the transmitting device and the amount of data being transmitted, with larger files requiring higher power, but there is always a carrier signal being transmitted *at all times*. Just as with DECT, the relative power densities are many times higher than any nearby phone mast.

> Frequency range: 2.4 and 5.8GHz

Older Wi-Fi routers had trouble matching the data transfer rates of a good wired LAN, however the latest 802.11ac protocol looks set to equal or even exceed wired speeds. Still, the Wi-Fi signal may be prone to dropouts and interference, and range is often limited by thick walls in the home, requiring additional booster routers to be installed. This is particularly true with routers operating in the 5GHz band as this frequency does not provide as good a range as the older 2GHz devices due to its lower penetrating power. Newer routers usually include both frequency bands.

With the cessation of analogue television and radio services, there are now 'white space' areas in the VHF and UHF frequency ranges (6-8MHz) that some countries have been experimenting with to provide so-called 'Super Wi-Fi' networks in rural areas, as the longer wavelengths enable better transmission rates. It has not been widely implemented as international regulations vary regarding use of these bands - for example they are also used for theatrical radio microphones, digital (DAB) radio and suchlike. Consequently it requires a very intelligent controller that can dynamically change channels to avoid interference from other devices. The particular frequency allocations also vary from country to country, so it is difficult to define an international standard.

With any Wi-Fi device there are data security issues, especially on unsecured open networks. Always make sure you have a good password set on your home Wi-Fi router and be wary of sending sensitive information (like your credit card details) over any unsecured network.

Wi-Fi enabled laptops emit power levels similar to a mobile phone handset. There are documented cases of male infertility caused by over-use of laptops being used on laps whilst sitting. Always try to use your laptop or tablet on a table and turn off the Wi-Fi when not in use.

Wireless headphones, games consoles, Bluetooth-enabled devices and many other gadgets use this same system, albeit at lower power levels. With the onslaught of the 'internet of things', more and more household devices are utilising this technology and are dependent on you having a working wireless network in the home.

Some Wi-Fi routers can act as 'femtocells' for other mobile phone or Wi-Fi users and may be transmitting at high levels without your knowledge. British Telecom for example use a small portion of each domestic Wi-Fi network to augment their 'BT Openzone' public Wi-Fi network in residential areas, so your router may still be transmitting even though you think it is not. Comcast

(Xfinity) in North America do the same with their routers.

Your router in some cases may also provide coverage for your mobile phone; this is especially likely if you do not have a fixed handset and use your mobile as your primary device to make calls in the home, something that is becoming increasingly common. The range of these femtocells is typically around 10m, but if provided by your operator they may allow it to be used for other users, so again it may be transmitting without your knowledge.

Solutions

There is really no need to have Wi-Fi switched on all the time in the home, school or office environment unless you are completely addicted to using a tablet or smartphone device. If you only have a fixed desktop computer, consider using a wired router. These are cheaply available for phone line, cable and fibre broadband users, and are actually more efficient than Wi-Fi as they are less prone to drop-outs and interference and usually have faster data transfer rates. They are also more secure.

If your existing wireless router is situated close to where you use your computer (which is often the case), connect to it directly using a standard Ethernet (LAN) cable and switch off the wireless transmission. Depending on the equipment supplied by your internet provider, this may be as simple as pressing a button on the router, or you may need to access the software control panel from your computer's internet browser and switch it off that way. Check the instructions from your provider.

If you need to extend your network and cannot install a wired LAN, you can connect your router to a dLAN or Powerline system that sends the data through your existing house wiring using a special mains adaptor. You connect your computer in the other room using a similar adaptor and a LAN cable. This is more secure than Wi-Fi, data transmission rates are many times faster, and the system is relatively cheap and very easy to use. See www.devolo.co.uk for an example or do a search for 'powerline adaptors'. Similar adaptors are available to extend the coverage of your Wi-Fi; in these the remote adaptor includes a small Wi-Fi transmitter. If you have these you should ensure that you switch them off when not in use. In larger houses, it is undoubtedly more preferable to use a few of these powerline transmitter-adaptors to create smaller Wi-Fi zones where they are needed, rather than using a more powerful main router and irradiating the entire household.

> If you are a British Telecom user you may also need to opt out of BT Openzone otherwise your router will still be transmitting to provide Wi-Fi coverage for others as part of the BT Openzone network. The downside of this is that you will have to relinquish your own free use of the Openzone network in other public areas if you have opted out. However, you can always replace the BT router with an equivalent model (one that you can disable the wireless function on) and still remain opted in to BT Openzone. This will require some technical knowledge, but it is not that difficult and many third-party routers (e.g. Netgear) are pretty much self-configuring for all internet providers, requiring you only to input your email address and Wi-Fi password.

If you cannot replace your Wi-Fi router, or if you simply cannot live without it because you need internet access on your tablet or smartphone, at least make sure you switch the router and any additional network extenders off when not in use, particularly at night. If you use a main desktop computer, you can easily connect your computer peripherals and router through an energy-saving demand switch that will automatically kill the power to all related devices when the main computer is shut down. These are readily available at hardware and electrical stores, usually in the form of a multi-socket plug board with a 'master' socket on it that controls the others.

'Smart' meters

'Smart' Meters

The UK government is insisting that we should all have 'Smart Meters' installed by 2020, at an estimated overall cost of 12 billion pounds. These so-called 'smart' meters have already been installed in several countries amidst a great deal of controversy not only regarding their safety, but also their effectiveness and longevity.

They are radio-frequency devices that will monitor your energy usage – either for water, electricity or gas – and communicate the meter readings directly back to the utility company using a combination of digital pulsed wireless protocols and other methods where wireless is not practical. The claims are that the devices will enable consumers to better monitor their own energy usage and thus save money; however quite the reverse has turned out to be the case in some areas where the meters have been installed and consumers have seen their energy bills actually rise significantly - some by more than 50%. Studies have demonstrated that the majority of consumers don't actually reduce their consumption even when they know what they're spending, and even the very best trials in the UK have seen only relatively minor savings of around 3% on bills.

There are safety concerns about the meters, with several recorded cases of meters overheating and bursting into flames without warning. Some 5,400 smart meters in Ontario had to be replaced following a series of fires.[17]

The scheme has been called a "colossal waste of money" by UK critics,[18] and Germany has already rejected EU demands for an 80% roll-out of smart meters on the grounds that it would be too costly for consumers. An estimated £50 per year will be added to the bills of UK consumers to pay for the scheme, whether or not they choose to have a smart meter installed. The projected total cost per household is between £200 and £400, although this is likely to be a conservative estimate.

Far from enabling consumers to save money, bills will be adjusted to charge higher rates at peak usage times. Of course companies may also promote discounted prices for energy use at off-peak times, but this is unlikely to change the habits of most consumers – who wants to do their laundry at midnight? Companies will also have the ability to cut off the utility remotely in cases of disputed bills or other conflicts.

The very nature of the digital technology exposes the possibility of somebody hacking the system, and it is not inconceivable that a hostile foreign power could take out the entire country with a targeted hack on the smart meter network. Being digital devices and with the speed at which such technology is evolving, the meters are also likely to have a short lifespan - some estimate as little as 5 to 7 years[19] - and will require frequent upgrades to both software and hardware; indeed some 600,000 of the estimated 1 million meters that British Gas have already installed as part of the UK programme need replacing as they are not considered 'smart' enough under present government regulations. If you change your energy supplier you are also likely to need your meter replaced to one that is compatible with their system.

Meters are designed to 'fail-to-off' in the event of any problems, which means that you could be left without any power, water or heating whenever your meter decides that it needs a software upgrade, or whenever the ambient temperature falls outside of its intended operating range. Some interesting research by independent UK consultant Dr Isaac Jamieson found that the temperature range specified for UK meters is between -10°C and +40°C. Although the upper limit is unlikely to be surpassed in the UK, there have certainly been several winters where the temperature has fallen below -10°C; you could find yourself without water or heating just when you are likely to need it the most! (In North America, the specified operational range is between -40°C and +85°C). [20]

There are major privacy concerns with the meters, as companies (and other interested parties) will be able to monitor energy usage directly and see exactly what appliances are in use at what times. In a worst-case scenario, this could mean that a criminal could hack into your home meter and know exactly where you are and what you are using at what times in order to plan a burglary. Of course your utility company will also have access to the same information, and stands to make vast amounts of money by selling such meta-data to third parties for marketing purposes. That's the real reason why they are so keen to see these meters installed in every home.

Frequency range: 900MHz, 2.4, 3.6 and 5.8GHz.

However, leaving these concerns aside, it is the RF radiation aspects of the meters that we are concerned with here. These devices will transmit pulsed Wi-Fi type signals at regular intervals around the clock, and in some areas meters may be linked together to provide local area Wi-Fi networks, increasing the radiation exposure for everyone.

A wireless smart meter typically has two radio transmitters for operating on two networks:
1. The Wide Area Network (WAN) links individual houses to a base station. If wireless, this can use mobile phone networks, Wi-Fi, or their own special frequencies. Some of these frequencies are low so as to penetrate further through concrete and into cellars. The base station could be located in the street and would collate information from a number of properties for transmission back to the utility company. In the UK it is proposed to use wired landline technology to connect base stations in apartment blocks and other situations where there are a large number of meters installed. How these base stations report back to the utility company will vary according to the location - they may utilise existing fibre-optic networks or phone landlines; or they may communicate using mobile network technology, which will require a huge increase in street-mounted microcells to be installed, most probably on lamp-posts or other 'smart' utility poles.

2. A Home Area Network (HAN) links the meter to appliances in the house. This will use wireless protocols like ZigBee, Z-wave or Wi-Fi (ZigBee and Z-wave are similar technologies to Bluetooth but have a lower data-transfer rate and lower power consumption – more on these in chapter 10). All of these systems can receive incoming wireless signals too, and the power densities will obviously need to be strong enough to penetrate the whole house.

Newer smart meters are designed to combine several different utilities, perhaps controlling electricity, gas and water supplies. These are obviously attractive to utility companies who supply more than one service to the household. If, on the other hand, your services are provided by separate suppliers, they are likely to each want to install their own smart meter, doubling or even tripling your exposure to these wireless emissions.

The latest smart meters can link together to form a 'mesh' or 'grid' system where each transmitter, instead of acting as a discrete unit communicating with the base station, can relay information to and from another meter, creating a true WAN network to aggregate the information from several meters for onward communication to the utility company. This is part of what is being called the 'smart grid', and reflects the increasing interconnectedness of everything in the digital age. The nodal points could be positioned (say) at the end of a street, on street lamps or utility poles. Such a network could also be used to provide other wireless services, for example public Wi-Fi networks, and your meter could be forming part of such systems without your knowledge or control. Indeed, Los Angeles recently became the first city in the world to install Philips' 'SmartPoles' LED street lighting where every lamp-post includes GPS sensors and 4G LTE transmitters to provide improved cell phone coverage and free public Wi-Fi, as well as enabling remote monitoring and control of the lights.[21] However in the UK, at least for now it seems that properties which voluntarily opt to have a wireless smart meter installed will remain discrete units with the meters sending and receiving their individual signals to and from the base stations.

Solutions

Despite what utility companies may tell you, there is no legal obligation to have one of these meters fitted and you are quite within your rights to refuse one. In 2012, the UK energy minister Charles Hendry told the House of Commons that, "We believe that people will benefit from having smart meters, but we will not make them obligatory. If people are concerned about the electromagnetic issues, they will not be required to have one."[22]

Despite this assurance, many big energy companies will try to browbeat you into accepting a smart meter. They do have a duty to provide a meter and connection to the supply, so they may try to claim that your old meter needs updating. Insist that they install a compatible analogue meter instead, even if you end up having to pay for it. Looking ahead, it seems very likely that increased pressure and even 'punishment payments' will be applied to consumers who continue to refuse installation of a smart meter.

See the Stop Smart Meters websites for more information and help on this subject. There are many useful resources there, including an email facility that will automatically record your desire to opt-out of a smart meter with every utility company. You will find the web addresses at the end of the book.

Mobile (Cellular) phones

Mobile (Cellular) phones

Where would we be without our mobile phones? It's hard to believe that these have only been around for about a quarter of a century. Despite the worries about health risks, not to mention the disfigurement of our countryside with the ever-increasing proliferation of phone masts, it is impossible to imagine modern life without these devices.

> I can still remember my first Motorola 'brick' back in the early 90s and the convenience that offered for making work calls away from home; now I carry a smartphone in my hand that has more processing power than a desktop PC did back then.

Hazards

The hazards of excessive cell phone use have been well documented. Many users will notice the warming effect in their ear after relatively short periods of use; those who use their phones extensively may develop more serious symptoms. The detrimental effects are particularly bad in children, where the skull has not attained its full thickness, which allows the microwaves from the phone to penetrate farther into the brain.

Remember that your phone needs to 'know' where it is, so it transmits to the nearest base station several times a minute just to 'check-in'. If the signal quality is poor, the phone will be transmitting at high power until it makes a connection.

Wired earpieces help, but these accessories should be used with caution if you are a heavy phone user, as the lead of the earpiece acts as an antenna and will channel the phone's microwaves straight into your ear. If the handset is worn on the belt or in a pocket at the time, the radiation from it penetrates the soft tissue of the body more than it does the skull, so you are actually increasing your exposure.

Bluetooth headsets use the same pulsed microwave frequencies as Wi-Fi. Although the power levels are lower, you still have a microwave transmitter in your ear. There is growing evidence of brain tumours and acoustic neuromas being linked to excessive use of Bluetooth headsets. More on this in Chapter Six.

Mobiles used as 'home phone' systems have a *femtocell* base station that may be transmitting data for other users *(see Chapter 3).* We are likely to see more of this type of combination base station as companies offer more permutations of network services, e.g. broadband, mobile and television packages.

Frequency range: Varies between countries, but usually between 800MHz – 2.6GHz

Solutions

Minimise microwave exposure by keeping calls short, or send text messages instead. Don't let your children have a mobile, or at least instruct them to use them for text messages only and make sure they are informed about safe protocols for using the phone as described here.

Do not leave your phone's Wi-Fi, Bluetooth or data roaming switched on when you're not using it. This has the added benefit of greatly extending the battery duration. (Although not as hazardous, turning off the GPS location setting will also work wonders in making your battery last longer.)

For maximum peace of mind you can switch the phone into 'flight mode' (or 'aircraft mode') when not in use, but of course this will prevent the phone from functioning as intended and effectively turns it into an expensive answering machine. If you are a light user of the phone this might be acceptable, providing you remember to turn it on periodically to check for messages. In most phones it is possible to still have Wi-Fi enabled when aircraft mode is selected, so make sure that you check this too.

Keep your phone in a handbag or briefcase, away from your body. There is evidence of men developing testicular or abdominal cancers or infertility from carrying their phone in their trouser pocket. Women are less prone to this sort of hazard as they usually have the phone in their handbag.

The Swiss Federal Office of public health recommends that cell phones should not be carried in a front trouser pocket when making calls and that it may be safest to hold the phone away from the body to reduce radiation. Studies have also found that metallic objects situated near your waistline, such as coins, a belt buckle, rings, keys etc. increased the Specific Absorption Rate (SAR) in the body at different frequencies.[23]

When making a call, do not bring the phone up to your ear until it starts ringing. The phone transmits at maximum power whilst it is searching for the nearest mast, but the power level drops dramatically once it has connected to the network. This single act alone will reduce your microwave exposure by roughly 90%.

Don't try to use the phone whilst in an aircraft or lift (elevator). The microwaves cannot easily pass through the metal skin, which acts as a Faraday cage, so the phone has to transmit at maximum power to get a signal. This increases the microwave density inside the aircraft as the microwaves bounce around the internal space, and will also cause your phone to drain battery power faster. The same goes for trains passing through a tunnel (indeed you are unlikely to get a signal at all in a long tunnel). Some airlines are now allowing phone use in the air, which requires that the aircraft will be fitted with a *picocell* transmitter with a satellite uplink. Although this makes it easier to get a good signal on the aircraft, bear in mind that using your phone is still liable to be very irritating to your fellow passengers.

Use speakerphone mode if possible, or if you are a heavy phone user consider purchasing an air-tube headset; these work by replacing the last section of wire at the earpiece with a length of tubing along which the sound is propagated acoustically, thus keeping the transducers (and the EMFs) away from your head. They are available from better health shops or online from many of the suppliers listed at the end of the book. Alternatively, you can fit a ferrite bead to your existing wired headset, which will greatly reduce the antenna effect (but not eliminate it completely).

You may also consider keeping your phone in a screened pouch or flip-case. These have a shielding panel on the front to reduce the microwave radiation passing into your head when on a call, and a rear cover that allows the microwaves from the antenna to pass unhindered. By always keeping the screened panel between the phone and your body, even when carrying it in your pocket, you can dramatically reduce your microwave exposure.

You will have to decide for yourself which of these solutions works best for you, based on your usage habits. If at all possible, I would recommend using both a screened case and an air-tube headset - as this will provide some level of protection in almost all circumstances.

A note on 'widgets' – there are many devices on the market that are worn on the body or attached to your phone that claim to either reduce the harmful radiation from the phone, or to neutralise the detrimental effect it has on the body. As there is even less scientific research pertaining to these devices, their efficacy is questionable at best and I have yet to be convinced that any of them are effective at reducing your exposure to the damaging microwaves, as the levels still register the same on a test meter.

Having said that, I will concede that it might be possible to reduce the *effect* the radiation is having on the body. Egyptian researcher Dr Ibrahim Karim has developed a system utilising geometric forms that he calls BioGeometry, and claims some remarkable successes in ameliorating the effects of RF radiation. A closely-monitored study conducted in the Swiss village of Hemberg where BioGeometry devices were installed throughout resulted in a significantly lower number of complaints from the residents about EHS symptoms.[24]

I have not seen enough scientific research to be convinced that anything is actually happening at a physiological level with these procedures. We may simply be seeing something like the placebo effect occurring, where the 'fix' is operating mainly at a psychological level by reducing our anxiety about the radiation. That's not to say they don't work - it is certainly worth experimenting with such complementary methods to see if they improve your symptoms, but I would advise that the sensible first line of defence should always be to minimise your exposure by screening and/or removing the radiation source. By all means supplement that with one of the 'alternative' remedies if you find that it works for you - there's nothing wrong with adopting a 'belt-and-braces' approach and doing as much as you can to protect yourself. But remember than any lifestyle changes intended to improve the immune system or work on the body's subtle energy systems are going to be compromised if you do not address the causative factor by removing the EMF stressor in the first place.

I once conducted an ad-hoc comparison between my own phone, which had a 'protective' widget stuck on the back, and an identical model owned by a friend. With my eyes closed and hands behind my back, I was able to identify my own phone 5 out of 5 times when both phones were placed in my hands. The only way I can describe it is that it somehow felt less 'buzzy' than the other phone. There was no other way I could tell the two phones apart. So there definitely seemed to be *something* going on, but I'm not sure what.

Bluetooth headsets and other 'wearable tech'

Bluetooth

Bluetooth is a low-power microwave transmission standard designed to connect devices together in a short-range personal network. It is named after the 10th Century Danish king Harald 'Bluetooth', who was the first to unite all the Danish tribes into a single kingdom.

Originally the standard was intended to link mobile phones and personal computers together, but it is more commonly used now to connect phones with Bluetooth-powered earpieces and, increasingly, other pieces of 'wearable tech' like Google Glass, VR headsets, fitness bands, portable loudspeakers, 'smart' watches and suchlike. It is also used for linking between games consoles and their controllers, 'smart' TV remote controls where infra-red was previously used, wireless sound distribution systems, and even to connect your mobile phone to your home DECT phone in some cases. Bluetooth is also pretty much a standard feature in all tablets and laptop computers, wireless keyboards and mice, printers etc., as well as in-car gadgets like sat-nav GPS devices.

Frequency range – 2.4GHz, the same as Wi-Fi.

Power – Class 4: 0.01 – 0.5mW. Class 3: 1mW. Class 2: 2.5mW. Class 1: up to 100mW. This is almost as high as some mobile phones.

Operating range – Class 3: up to 1m. Class 2: up to 10m. Class 1 & 4: up to 100m.

The lowest power Bluetooth devices are Class 4, this is also known as 'Bluetooth Smart' as it uses very little power so is commonly utilised for data transmission between smartphones and peripherals such as smart watches, fitness bands and similar devices (it does not have the bandwidth to support voice communications). Class 3 is an older standard and has now been largely supplanted by Class 2 which provides greater range. The even more powerful Class 1 devices are intended for longer range connections but are already being used in some headset devices.

There is some overlap in function between Bluetooth and Wi-Fi protocols, particularly with the increased range of the latest Bluetooth standards; and indeed both technologies utilise the same 2.4GHz frequency band, although Bluetooth is generally lower powered. The Apple Watch, for example, uses both Bluetooth 4.0 LE and Wi-Fi 802.11 protocols. We are likely to see more of this crossover between protocols when the new 5G standard is implemented. The proposed protocol specifies that devices should be able to access several wireless access technologies simultaneously and be able to move seamlessly between them.

Security can again be an issue with these devices. A recent study demonstrated that it a smart watch's motion sensors can be used to guess what keys your left hand is pressing, and thus to extrapolate, with a frighteningly high degree of accuracy, what is being typed on your computer keyboard. You can imagine a scenario where a bogus pedometer app loaded innocently into the watch is secretly supplying your keystroke information to cyber-criminals, enabling them to gather sensitive information such as your passwords or credit card numbers.[25]

Hazards

Although the power levels are much lower than those emitted by mobile phones, Bluetooth still carries many of the same hazards, particularly in relation to the digital pulsed frequencies. There has been comparatively little study on the dangers of the technology and Bluetooth devices are not subject to the same SARs testing as mobile phones, which leads many 'experts' (who are likely in the pay of the manufacturers) to claim that it is safe. However this claim is not based on research – quite the reverse in fact. There simply hasn't been enough research conducted yet to make a conclusion one way or the other, although there are many claims linking Bluetooth radiation to such ailments as blindness, deafness, neck pain, skin rashes, headaches, tinnitus, and brain tumours - even hair loss and Alzheimer's disease.

In the case of a Bluetooth device worn on the head, for example audio headphones, a phone headset or Google Glass, the main hazard will be from prolonged exposure to the radiation in your ear; but as the device works in conjunction with your phone, you are being exposed to a double-whammy of radiation from both devices *all the time* when the two are 'paired' with each other. At least one study has found reduced fertility in men who carry their phone in a trouser pocket while using a Bluetooth headset.[26]

There is plenty of evidence that Bluetooth is bad for you - there have been several reports from users of Bluetooth headsets and Google Glass of headaches, blurred vision, anxiety and depression – all typical symptoms of electro-stress. There have even been reports of headset users developing acoustic neuromas after many years of use, and I am personally aware of two long-term Bluetooth headset wearers who died from brain tumours discovered on the same side of the head as their headset was worn. I have also seen reports of smartwatch wearers suffering skin rashes on their wrist, although it is not clear if this is in any way related to the device use.

When used in a vehicle, such as a car hands-free kit, the metal frame of the vehicle acts as a Faraday cage, making the microwave radiation bounce around the inside of the vehicle bathing you and your passengers in a sea of radiation. As more new cars are supplied with Bluetooth installed as standard, this is likely to become more of a problem. The same goes for phone usage in cars generally – be a safer driver and turn your phone off when driving. You are an estimated four times more likely to have an accident if you use a hand-held phone while driving or riding a motorbike, which is why it is illegal in the UK. Although hands-free kits are technically legal, if the police think that you are distracted while in charge of the vehicle, you can still be charged with reckless driving.

> I stopped using a Bluetooth device in the car as I found that I was getting a headache from the proximity of the hands-free kit clipped on the sun visor. I also found that having to fiddle with it when answering a call was distracting from my driving, so now I simply switch the phone to aircraft mode when I'm driving and pick up messages whenever I stop. It's safer on all counts.

Solutions

There really isn't much option with Bluetooth other than to stop using it. Avoid using a Bluetooth headset and don't wear any Bluetooth-enabled devices such as music headphones, fitness bands or smart watches, especially if they utilise the high-power Class 1 or Class 2 protocols. Many models of smart watch require Wi-Fi to be enabled too, thus increasing your exposure; and remember that your phone is also transmitting all the time if you use these devices. If you are at all sensitive, it is best to avoid Bluetooth completely.

If you simply must wear a Bluetooth headset for work, if possible don't keep it in your ear when switched on but not in use; at least that will reduce the exposure levels in your head. You should also avoid Class 1 Bluetooth devices, which are some 40 times more powerful than Class 2.

Consider using an air-tube headset to connect to your phone instead. It may not be as convenient as your Bluetooth headset, but it is many times safer. These are becoming more readily available as concerns over long-term wearing of Bluetooth headsets increase. (*See also* Chapter Five regarding shielding options for the phone)

Also make sure that any laptops, tablets and similar devices have the Bluetooth switched off if you are not using it. You would be surprised how many gadgets have Bluetooth these days.

External phone masts

External mobile phone masts

Can you remember what the countryside looked like before the advent of the mobile phone? It is hard to imagine nowadays, with phone masts cropping up in the most out-of-the-way locations, atop hills, in the middle of forests, beside remote roads and rail lines, often in the most unexpected places.

You can tell phone masts by the long rectangular transmitter boxes they have, usually arranged in a circular array round the mast. These are designed to radiate in a comparatively narrow wedge-shaped beam horizontally from the transmitter. Perversely, this often means that directly underneath the mast is the area with lowest power density. The beam shape isn't perfect so there are some scatter spikes extending upwards and downwards from the transmitter that may generate hotspots, but the majority of the beam is directed outwards so that the main power density will be experienced between roughly 50 and 200 metres from the mast. The many campaigns by concerned parents to have masts removed from the roofs of school buildings often backfire by causing the masts to be re-sited nearby with direct line-of-sight of the school. This often has the unfortunate result of increasing the microwave density in the building by siting it squarely in the beam of the transmitters.

Hazards

Unless you have direct line-of-sight view of a mobile mast within 300m of your property, the microwave power density levels in the home are likely to be much lower than those from internal DECT or Wi-Fi as much of the radiation from the mast will be absorbed by intervening buildings and walls. In theory, the power density is designed to be highest between 50-200m from the mast, but this is rarely the case in practice and hotspots can arise at closer distances.

In dense urban areas, check for *microcells* on the front of buildings. These often look like unmarked burglar alarm boxes painted to match the building, but will have relatively thick cables entering the underside of the box. If you have one of these on your exterior wall, you should consider screening on the inside wall with suitable material.

Picocells are even smaller transmitters often used inside shopping centres and other public areas. These are hard to spot. Petrol station forecourt signs and church spires often conceal mobile transmitters, and some are even disguised as trees in rural areas, complete with fake foliage to mask the transmitter modules. They are even now being included in street lighting poles in several major cities (see Chapter 4).

TETRA (TErrestrial Trunked RAdio) is a bespoke communications system used by police and other emergency services. In practice it works like a cross between a mobile phone and a walkie-talkie. TETRA masts look a little like conventional aerials with four paperclip-like nodules on the side. These transmit at a lower power than conventional masts and do not pulse quite as aggressively; however they do pulse continuously day and night and some people report greater sensitivity to TETRA than other phone masts.

The handsets used in TETRA systems are more hazardous for users, as the signal pulse frequency from them is 17.6Hz, which is extremely close to human brain wave frequencies. Signals around the 16Hz frequency have been shown to increase leakage of calcium ions (essential components of many biological functions) from the brain and other tissues. TETRA signals have also been known to interfere with vehicle electronic locking mechanisms and alarms. The system is now rather dated and overdue for replacement, with the most likely option under discussion being to utilise the 4G mobile networks. However there are practical concerns that still need to be addressed.

The circular drum-like structures that you may see on some phone masts are tight-beam point-to-point microwave links used to transmit data between towers, and are unlikely to cause a problem unless you are directly in the path of the beam.

Radar stations are an oft-overlooked hazard, and the regular sweep of a radar dish (usually every 5-10 seconds) can be detected many miles away from the source. See the link at the end of the book to the online video showing aphids reacting to a radar beam 14 miles away. If you suffer from EHS and live near an airport or sea port you should check for radar sources.

Other potential causes of problems are local radio systems used by taxi operators, amateur 'ham' radio enthusiasts, emergency services, military installations and the like – if you have one of their transmitter aerials that is extremely close to your property it may have an adverse effect on you if you are particularly sensitive, purely because of the high power density from the antenna. However, for most people they shouldn't be a problem as the frequency range is usually the more conventional VHF/UHF bands of FM radio.

Solutions

Find your local masts at -
http://www.sitefinder.ofcom.org.uk – this will show the
location of all local masts and microcells as blue
triangles and give details of the mast operator,
transmission system, height, and power density levels.
Note some mobile operators are currently opted out of
this scheme so the information is frequently out of date.
In the USA try http://www.antennasearch.com/

Stone walls absorb much of the radiation, especially in
older houses; however conventional (sash) windows do
not. Newer double-glazing with thermal protection film
(Pilkington K) can absorb over 95% of the radiation -
but the frames, which are usually uPVC, will not.

You can apply a clear plastic screening film to the
windows (but see above regarding the frames), or you
could have some net curtains made from metal-
impregnated screening material. You need to ensure
that these fit tightly to the whole window opening as
microwaves can get through very small gaps. In some
situations it may be easier to install a separate internal
frame with the material attached.

If you need to take additional precautions, screening
materials, window films and carbon paint can be bought
via www.emfields-solutions.com and several other
suppliers. See the resources section at the end of the
book.

Microwave smog from neighbours

Microwave smog from neighbouring properties (DECT phones, Wi-Fi etc.)

This is unlikely to be a major problem unless you live in an apartment block or a terraced house with shared party walls. You will usually get far greater levels of exposure from external phone masts or sources within your own home. Even if you have a phone mast at the bottom of your garden, you will experience greater exposure levels from having a DECT cordless phone inside the house.

In tightly-packed housing estates you may be able to pick up a Wi-Fi signal from a neighbouring house, but the intensity of the signal is liable to be pretty low. Apartments are likely to have more problems from neighbours, either from a DECT phone or Wi-Fi router placed against a party wall, or more likely through the floors from apartments above or below in older buildings.

Earlier I related my own story regarding a downstairs neighbour and her DECT phone that was keeping us both awake at night. In my apartment I can still pick up 3 or 4 different wireless networks from neighbours on my phone or laptop in certain rooms, although thankfully the levels are fairly low. In situations like these you either have to try and convince your neighbours to change their own habits, or resort to screening your own place as much as you can.

Modern buildings are likely to have plasterboard (Drywall) ceilings which have a foil backing for insulation purposes but is also pretty effective at blocking microwaves, so leakage from above or below might not be such an issue.

Hazards

Exposure hazards are identical to those previously listed for use of Wi-Fi or DECT phones inside the home, except that the levels will be comparatively lower of course. It depends on the location of the offending device in the neighbouring property.

The most common sources from your neighbours are likely to be Wi-Fi and DECT cordless phones, but as more wireless gadgets come on to the market, the possible sources are bound to increase. Games consoles, baby monitors, wireless television sharing devices (e.g. Slingbox) and other internet-connected devices may be transmitting high enough levels to cause problems in your own property. The roll-out of so-called 'smart' utility meters is also a concern here, especially if you live in an apartment block where there is likely to be a centralised transmitter to aggregate the data from every apartment. If this is situated directly outside your apartment it is liable to be problematic.

Femtocells are the smallest transmitters that your phone company will often try to sell to you to enhance your mobile signal at home. Frequently these are combined with your wireless broadband router if you have a combination phone and broadband deal with your service provider. These can be troublesome if your neighbour has one installed. There are likely to be more of these installed in conjunction with smart meters to provide the Home Area Network that such meters require.

The mains wiring inside houses can sometimes resonate with certain microwave frequencies, as can metal-framed beds and mattress springs. Lighting circuits are likely to be the worst culprits here, particularly in apartment buildings where wiring in your ceiling and light pendants might be radiating microwaves from the floor above. A dangling light pendant of the right length can be a remarkably efficient transmitting antenna of mobile phone frequencies.

Solutions

Party walls can be screened with carbon paint, metallic foils etc. You can also buy specially-treated wallpaper that will block or absorb radiation from neighbours. Even regular aluminium foil will work, although it is not very robust and so is not recommended.

Some building insulating materials with metallic coatings can be very effective and are relatively cheap, but make sure it is real metal, not a plasticised layer. Foil-backed plasterboard (Drywall) can work well. Test the foil layer with a cheap resistance meter to make sure that it is actually conductive, and cover all the joints with foil tape to ensure conductivity between sections. To reduce electric fields as well as provide insulation from microwaves, you could also connect the foil panels to earth using a grounding lead.

As mentioned in the previous section, you can also purchase metal-impregnated fabric that can be made up into curtains or screen panels to cover windows and doors. Most modern double-glazing incorporates a special thermal coating (Pilkington K) that has the added benefit of blocking over 95% of microwaves so you may not need this. However microwaves can still penetrate around the frame edges, and of course when the window is open this protection is eliminated.

At the very least you should try to screen your bedroom as much as possible, as it is likely that this is where you will spend the most time and during sleep is when the body's immune system repairs itself. You can buy complete bed canopies (like a mosquito net) made of conductive gauze fabric. If you can also screen the floor underneath the bed this is a good recommended minimum level of protection in the home. It is also possible to purchase complete bed sheets made of conductive material that can be earthed to provide protection (*see chapter 11*).

Pendant light fittings can be fitted with ferrite beads on the cable to prevent them acting as antennas. These are relatively cheap and easy to use, they simply clip around the cables and don't require any wiring skills.

See http://www.emfields-solutions.com for suitable products.

A Basic Guide to Technopathic Stress

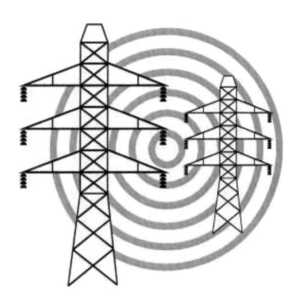

Power Frequency EMFs

Power frequency EMFs

The term 'power frequency' refers to the low-frequency electric and magnetic fields generated by conventional electrical devices and mains wiring. The normal frequency in the UK is 50Hz, and 60Hz in the USA and Canada. It is important to understand the difference between electric and magnetic fields. *Electric* fields are produced by a wire having a voltage (potential) on it in respect to earth, and will be present whenever an appliance is plugged in, even if it is switched off at the appliance. A *magnetic* field is produced around the cable whenever the appliance is switched on and current is flowing. The larger the current, the higher the magnetic field will be. Think of it like the difference between a water hose connected to the tap but with the hose nozzle closed – there is still pressure (potential) in the hose even though there is no water flow; this equates to the electric field. The same hose with the nozzle open and water flowing is analogous to the magnetic field.

External high-voltage power lines and substations can be problematic when they are close to your residence. There have been several studies linking proximity to overhead power lines and childhood leukaemia, although some researchers claim that a direct causal link has yet to be established. A 2005 study conducted by the University of Oxford in conjunction with Transco, the UK national grid owners, found that children whose birth address was within 200 metres of an overhead power line had a 70% increased risk of contracting leukaemia. Children living 200 to 600m away from power lines had a 20% increased risk.[27] Although the report was cautious about directly blaming the EMFs for causing the leukaemia, there is no question that many people nowadays will not buy a house in close proximity to power lines, and house prices are likely to be depressed in such locations. There are enough records of 'cancer clusters' in these areas for many local authorities to leave wide gaps in housing schemes where there are overhead lines. Such construction is already banned in the US and Sweden, and the US National Institute of Health states that overhead power lines should be considered as possible causes of human cancer.

A much-disputed study conducted in 2000 by Prof Denis Henshaw at Bristol University suggests that the danger from power lines lies less with the EMFs and more with ionisation of the air around the cables, which will give an electrical charge to any pollution particles in the vicinity, making them more likely to attach to lung tissue. Lines close to major roads or industrial sites are obviously worse in this regard, especially with the particulate exhaust fumes from diesel engines and emissions from factories.[28]

Hazards

Inside the home, the main culprits are magnetic fields from transformers and switched mode power supplies, such as bedside alarm clocks, phone chargers, laptops and other gadgets. These generally look like large plugs, or sometimes they are in a separate power supply unit like a small box – laptop computers frequently have these. If the item doesn't have a visible transformer either in the plug or a separate PSU, it probably has one inside it. Beware of items like bedside clocks or lamps with internal transformers.

Magnetic fields from cables in or behind walls, or under floors in apartment blocks can also be problematic.

Lighting circuits, because of the way in which they are wired and also because they are likely to be under the floors of upstairs rooms (which are frequently bedrooms) are often the worst offenders.

In the UK and a few other countries,[29] the normal configuration for domestic wiring is the ring circuit, where both ends of a circuit are linked together at the consumer unit. This allows greater capacity on the circuit compared to radial wiring where each circuit consists of a single line of sockets. Ring circuits were introduced in the UK after the Second World War, mainly as an economy measure to save on copper.

In a radial circuit, by contrast, the magnetic fields produced by the current flowing down the live conductor and back along the neutral are more or less equal and opposite, cancelling each other out. This form of wiring produces the lowest magnetic fields. However, this is not the case in ring circuits where the current has a choice of direction to return to the consumer unit, meaning that the opposing fields do not cancel each other out. This results in a higher magnetic field being radiated from the cables. In lighting circuits (because of the way they are wired) the live and neutral wires are often separated, which again results in unbalanced fields. Two-way lighting circuits are the worst in this regard.

> In a house with complex dimmer circuiting on all lights throughout, I measured a field of over 1000V/m at half a meter distance from a bedside dimmer switch that was one half of a two-way system. The opposing switch at the other side of the bed measured only 10V/m, which is more normal for domestic wiring.

Apartment buildings may have high electric and magnetic fields radiating through the walls from appliances or wiring in neighbouring apartments. Your bed may be adjacent to a microwave oven, consumer unit, fridge or even the mains intake of the next apartment.

A client whose bed head was against the party wall in his apartment had developed serious sinus cancer and required surgery. When I checked the electric and magnetic fields I found extremely high readings right where his pillow was located, suggesting some power-hungry appliance or possibly the electricity meter against the wall on the other side. Needless to say we immediately moved his bed to the other side of the room.

High-voltage power lines within 500m of the building are an obvious hazard. The bigger the pylon, the higher the voltage, and the more hazardous it is likely to be. Lower voltage utility lines, such as street lighting cables, attached to the external wall may also present problems if a bed is next to that wall.

Electricity substations and transformers immediately outside the building, adjacent to the wall or perhaps mounted on a post are another potential hazard. If a substation is some distance away it is unlikely to be a major problem unless the cables for it run close to the property, which may introduce high magnetic fields into the building. If the cables are laid adjacent to water pipes entering the building, the water pipes can carry an induced current. In newer properties this is unlikely to happen as there should be a plastic isolation segment fitted to the water pipe where it enters the property, and increasingly in urban situations the mains water pipes are now plastic.

TVs and computer screens – the older cathode ray tubes are known to give off high levels of EMFs, particularly from the rear or the unit. However these displays are now almost universally redundant, having been replaced by newer flat screen LCD/LED types that give off much less radiation.

Solutions

With all EMFs, the Inverse Square Law applies – this means that power levels fall off very quickly with distance from the source. So for example, if the appliance is 2 feet away from you, the intensity of the field will be 4 times less; if it is 4 feet away, the intensity is 16 times less and so on. Either move the item, or move yourself to a safe distance.

Keep any transformers and devices with internal transformers at least 2-3 feet away if you can; especially bedside clock radios, phone chargers and other devices. Don't charge your mobile phone on your bedside table. Keep wiring away from under the bed, and ideally switch off and unplug all non-essential items around the bed at night.

Don't site beds against a wall if you know there are any power cables or appliances behind it. That includes the electricity meter – I have seen more than one house where the bed was directly through the wall from a cupboard housing the main electricity intake. Check the outside walls for street lighting cables or other municipal power lines attached to the wall. In apartment buildings, it is best to keep your bed away from any party walls if you can, as you never know what appliances your neighbours might have placed against it on the other side.

If you are doing any rewiring in your house, try to make sure that any cabling is installed in metal conduit or trunking to minimise the electric fields. You can also buy extension leads with armoured cable that is screened with a metal braid mesh. These are good for use in the vicinity of the bed.

If you have a small substation immediately adjacent to your house, there isn't much you can do about it except try to keep beds as far away as you can; but one at the bottom of the garden shouldn't be a problem. Levels of EMFs from these small substations fall to background levels within about 3-4m. Stone walls should reduce any electric fields to manageable levels, or you can cover the wall with screening material; however this does little to reduce the penetration of any magnetic field. Proximity of a substation is also likely to have a negative effect on the resale value of the property.

With high-voltage overhead power lines a safe distance should be at least 25m for 11kV lines (these are usually carried on wooden 'telegraph poles' with transformer boxes mounted on the pole at the edge of the property), and 250m for 400kV lines (the biggest metal pylons carrying electricity long distances across country). If you have a large pylon near the house there's not much you can do apart from moving house. If there is a transformer box on a pole that is too close to the house you could try asking the electricity company to move it.

Ideally all overhead power lines would be buried underground, which would eliminate the ionised pollution aspect completely and reduce the electromagnetic fields to safer levels, however it is obviously considerably more expensive to do this. If you own the land that power lines cross, in theory you have legal recourse under Wayleave or Easement rights to ask the utility company to either move or bury the cables; however there are a number of factors involved here and it may not always be possible to achieve a satisfactory or economically viable arrangement with all the parties concerned.

Wireless baby monitors, burglar alarms, games consoles, tablets, laptops and other sources of RF radiation

Digital wireless baby monitors

These modern units use exactly the same technology as DECT cordless phones and Wi-Fi, with the same attendant issues – i.e. continual high levels of pulsed microwave radiation. Wireless video monitoring systems have the same problems. These systems frequently cannot be used where there is Wi-Fi because they can cause interference, and they have been known to interfere with other devices operating on the same frequencies (and vice-versa). Some models use Wi-Fi to link to your tablet or smartphone – besides the radiation issues, these are also at risk from hacking.

Beware especially of models with cordless motion sensor mats placed under the baby. These will transmit high power densities of microwaves right into the cot (and through your baby) and are best avoided. Older analogue models are still the best option if you can find one, but even these should be kept at least 2 feet from the baby's head. The signal from these is not secure (it can be picked up on FM radios with the correct frequency) and is more liable to interference from other equipment, but they are safer than the digital models as they operate on more conventional VHF/UHF radio frequencies. These are becoming harder to find, but there are still a few analogue models on the market. Look for a multi-channel model, which will minimise interference problems. Some digital systems use the mains wiring to send the signal to another part of the house but don't transmit a DECT signal; these are fine.

> Frequency range: Analogue - 40, 49 or 900MHz
> DECT digital - 1.9GHz
> Other digital - usually 900MHz and 2.4GHz

Games consoles

Most games consoles have Wi-Fi capability to connect to the internet, and many use Wi-Fi or Bluetooth to connect to remote controllers. Surprisingly, many of these consoles continue to transmit Wi-Fi radiation *even when they are apparently switched off.* You need to physically disconnect the unit at the mains to stop it transmitting the Wi-Fi signal. Even small hand-held consoles may have inbuilt Wi-Fi, such as the Nintendo 3DS for example.

Motion detectors in burglar alarms

Older systems used infra-red detectors, which are fine; but newer systems are mostly microwave-based, again with the same attendant problems as DECT and Wi-Fi. Check your user instructions to see if the sensors can be disabled when you are in the house, or try to use a system with infra-red sensors.

Tablets, laptops, televisions and other 'smart' gadgets.

As more and more people own iPads, tablets and other similar gadgets, the need for all-pervasive Wi-Fi networks becomes increasingly demanding. Gadget manufacturers seem intent on equipping everything they can think of with wireless communication capability, from fridges and cookers all the way down to children's toys. At the moment, all of these devices presume that you have a functioning Wi-Fi network in the house, and of course the retailers will be quick to encourage you to install one if you haven't already. Most of these devices will have the Wi-Fi enabled by default, so you may already be subjected to unwanted microwave radiation.

Privacy issues are often overlooked in the rush to sell more 'smart things'. Electronics giant Samsung have been criticised for their cavalier attitude to privacy with their voice-controlled, Wi-Fi enabled 'smart' televisions when it was revealed that the TVs collect everything that is said and send the data to Samsung and a third-party company, who then convert the speech into text before sending it back to Samsung. Although Samsung quickly pointed out that this only happens if the user has activated the voice-recognition feature on the remote, it transpired that the data was being sent with no encryption, meaning that anyone with moderate hacking skills could potentially harvest sensitive information from your living room without your knowledge or consent.[30] Samsung are not the only manufacturer doing this - US company Verizon, for instance, filed a patent in 2012 that allows the television to watch *you*, with built-in facial, profile and gesture recognition software so that it can monitor the number of people in the room, their sex, race, what they are doing and even what they are eating while watching television. The goal of this is to provide what Verizon call 'targeted advertising', but the Orwellian implications of this sort of unwarranted monitoring are obvious.[31]

There are also 'personal' devices like smart watches, fitness bands, heart rate monitors, bathroom scales, plant monitors, flying 'drones', model cars, cooking thermometers - even toothbrushes; all designed to connect to either your home Wi-Fi network and/or your Bluetooth-enabled smartphone. I even recently saw a crowd-funded 'menstrual cup' with Bluetooth capability that over 3,500 backers are willing to see go into production!

You can switch off the Wi-Fi in your laptop and tablet when you don't need to use it, and this will certainly help prolong the battery usage. If your tablet has 3G or 4G data connectivity built in, it is often better to use this than your house Wi-Fi network as the signal is likely to be less powerful (and so less damaging), and 4G often provides better speeds than Wi-Fi these days - providing you have a suitable data package of course. As with mobile phones, try not to use these devices on your lap or close to your head.

As more Wi-Fi enabled gadgets come into our lives it is likely that more homes are going to require Wi-Fi networks. Hopefully some of the protocols and suggestions in this book will give you enough information to keep your exposure to a minimum. Most importantly, you should aim to keep your bedroom a wireless-free zone to ensure a good night's sleep.

The 'Internet of Things'

As we have seen, increasing numbers of devices are appearing on the market that can communicate with each other and the household systems to create the 'smart' interconnected home. Even now you can buy energy monitoring meters, colour-changing LED lightbulbs, security cameras, heating controls, refrigerators, key finders, light switches, kettles, garage door openers… the list is ever-growing. All of these devices can be controlled over the internet via your home Wi-Fi connection. As more of them are introduced, the limited bandwidth available on the already-crowded radio frequency spectrum means that the possibility of interference with other devices multiplies. It is increasingly difficult for regulators to assign frequency bands for all the diverse devices that are appearing, and this results in more gadgets interfering with each other, the home phone or Wi-Fi systems, as well as television and other broadcasting networks. Inevitably, it also increases the chances of someone on the internet being able to hack into your home network and take control of them.

One of the other downsides of the escalating numbers of these devices is that we are running out of individual internet addresses for them. The present Internet Protocol (IP) addressing system is IPv4 – the IP address is the long number that provides an individual address for each device on the internet and allows communication between them. Usually the format is a group of four numbers, something like 172.16.255.1. This notation has been in use since 1981 and can provide individual addresses for around 4.3 billion devices. Despite clever restructuring, by 2012 it was clear that the world was soon going to run out of IP addresses, and this is actually limiting the deployment of the all-connected world of technology that we seem to be inevitably heading towards.

The introduction of the replacement protocol IPv6 is presently underway, however the two protocols are not completely inter-compatible, which complicates the changeover process somewhat so it will be a few years yet until IPv6 is fully implemented.

ZigBee and Z-wave

It's worth mentioning here a couple of other RF communication protocols that are already in use - ZigBee and Z-wave; the former operating in the same 2.4GHz frequency range as existing Wi-Fi and phone networks and the latter being assigned the lower 900MHz band. Both ZigBee and Z-wave are specifically designed to operate at very low-power, low bandwidth and at short range compared to Wi-Fi or Bluetooth, so you will find them used mostly in battery-operated gadgets like remote controls and heating regulators that only need to communicate infrequently. Generally these should not be a problem to EHS sufferers as the power is so low. ZigBee is one of the proposed standards for use in Home Area Networks for smart meters, but some operators think that it is not suitable in many locations with older, more solidly built houses where thickness of walls would limit its effectiveness.

Eleven

Beds

Beds – Really?

"How can my bed be a problem?" I hear you cry. There are a number of technopathic factors relating to beds, and as the bedroom is where you are likely to spend most of your time it is worth paying particular attention to the space to ensure that you can make it as safe as possible. The time spent asleep is when the body's immune system repairs the damage and gets rid of toxins accumulated during the day, so it makes sense that we should give it as much support as possible. The bedroom should be your haven from EMFs, so take some time to reduce exposure here as much as you can.

Electric blankets

These generate very high levels of electric and magnetic fields. If you sleep with the electric blanket switched on, you are exposing yourself to these EMFs for hours at a time. This constitutes *chronic exposure*.

The solution is simple - do not sleep with the blanket switched on. Warm the bed beforehand, then switch off and **unplug** the blanket before getting into bed. Remember that, like water in a hosepipe with the tap turned off, the electric field is still present even when the blanket is switched off at the controller.

Other electrical items

Try to minimise the number of gadgets you have in your bedroom, and especially keep the area around and under the bed free of cables, extension cords and electrical items. Clock radios are some of the worst emitters of EMFs, particularly if they have an internal transformer. Luckily many of the modern devices have a separate power supply and it is usually possible to site this away from the bed. Remember that EMFs are subject to the inverse-square law, so you can minimise your exposure by keeping electrical items two or three feet away from the bed. Better still, use a battery-operated clock.

Spring mattresses and bed bases

Metal bed frames and wire-sprung mattresses can cause problems by amplifying and re-radiating microwaves and other EMFs. The springs can act as waveguides and focus the EMFs into tight hotspots.

> I have seen clients who have DECT phones or Wi-Fi elsewhere in the house where the levels in the bedroom were relatively low – until the meter was held over the bedsprings, whereupon the EMF levels skyrocketed.

Additionally, there is some evidence to suggest that the metal wiring in a mattress or bed base, if it is of a particular length, can harmonically resonate with television and FM radio transmission signals in exactly the same way as any receiving antenna and produce a standing wave of elevated EMF levels above the mattress. It has been suggested that this may be responsible for an increase in left-sided cancers in the Western world (because most people sleep on their right side).[32]

The metal springs also distort the Earth's natural geomagnetic field and can produce quite severe hot spots. There is a simple test you can do with an ordinary magnetic compass, simply by holding it just above the mattress and moving it around slowly. You will easily be able to identify areas where the springs are distorting the magnetic field. If the needle deviates by 20 degrees or more I would strongly recommend replacing the mattress.

Use wooden-framed beds and mattresses without springs, such as a memory foam mattress or futon. Any new mattress (particularly foam ones) will have its own problems as they are usually impregnated with fire-retardant chemicals that many researchers regard as toxic. It is possible to find naturally fire-retardant organic mattresses made from natural latex and I would recommend one of these if possible. They are manufactured in the UK by Abaca Organic - http://www.abacaorganic.co.uk/

Water beds
Although the heating pads in older waterbeds could generate high electric and magnetic fields, the newer models are generally pretty good if the heater pad is not directly underneath the body and the bed frame is non-metallic. The heater in a water bed is a compact pad positioned underneath the mattress and it only operates intermittently at moderately low power, so the levels of EMFs above the mattress are fairly low. The supply cable and thermostat can produce slightly elevated electric fields, but nowhere near those produced by an electric blanket. If you are at all worried about it you can switch it off and unplug it overnight, as you would an electric blanket; but you must remember to switch it back on again in the morning if you want your bed to retain its temperature. Another benefit of water beds is that the thick pad of water actually provides a pretty good barrier against geopathic and electromagnetic stress from below.

Bed canopies
In severe situations where levels of EMFs in the bedroom are extremely high and you are unable to

properly screen the entire room, or if you are highly electro-sensitive, it may be worth considering a bed canopy made from metal-impregnated gauze material, which completely surrounds the bed just like a mosquito net. You will also need some screening material to go underneath the bed or a full-cover earthing sheet, but a canopy and earthing sheet can often be the most cost-effective solution to your EMF problems. It can also add a touch of exotic glamour to the bedroom!

Earthing sheets

The principle of sleeping 'earthed' is based on the concept that we are insulated from the Earth in our modern lives because of the preponderance of synthetic clothing, shoes, carpets and fabrics, which leads to an accumulation of voltage in the body throughout the day. You can often notice this when you get a static 'zap' from touching a metal handrail or doorknob, when the voltage is discharged. People who walk barefoot and sleep directly on the ground do not suffer from this as their electrical potential is always the same as that of the Earth. By bringing the body back to this equal potential, we allow electrons from the earth to flow into the body and neutralise the free radicals that have accumulated, allowing the immune system to function optimally. Many athletes sleep in earthed sleeping bags during competitions as it accelerates tissue repair and eases muscle pain and stiffness.

This is a large subject and worth investigating further to appreciate the full benefits of 'earthing', but in the context of this guide it is important as many EHS sufferers have found benefits from sleeping earthed, mainly from the enhancement to the immune system that it provides. In addition, studies suggest that maintaining good grounding of the body actually provides protection against the effects of EMFs by creating an 'umbrella effect.' When grounded, the body's potential becomes an extension of the Earth's giant electrical system, and this actively repels ambient electric and magnetic fields from the body.

Typically, an earthing sheet comprises a wide strip of conductive fabric that is laid *underneath* the normal bed sheet, and is then connected via a special grounding plug to the nearest socket with an earth connector (which need not be switched on). The plug has a resistor fitted to prevent any current flowing outwards into the sheet in the event of an electrical fault or overload. You can also connect the lead directly to a metal pipe or earthing rod sunk into the ground outside the house if such an arrangement is convenient. The sheet should be positioned where it will be closest to an uncovered part of the body – so usually down at the foot of the bed is fine. Sheets that cover the whole bed are also available.

> The effect of sleeping earthed is quite subtle, but most people do notice a distinct difference in sleep quality after a short period of time, and for myself I have certainly noticed a more rapid relief from aching muscles after sleeping earthed.

For more details, I recommend the book *'Earthing – the most important health discovery ever?'* by Clinton Ober, Stephen T. Sinatra MD, and Martin Zucker.

Twelve

Dirty Electricity

Dirty Electricity

Dirty electricity (DE) is a term applied to higher-frequency interference carried on the mains wiring. Typically the frequencies involved lie between those of power-level EMFs and the microwave bands. In an ideal world, the alternating current of our domestic mains electricity would produce a smooth sine-wave pattern when plotted on an oscilloscope, like this:

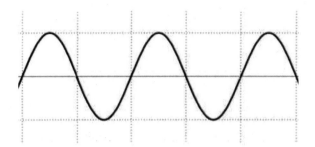

However, things are rarely as perfect as this outside of the laboratory, and the signal from the wiring in your house is more likely to look like this (actually, probably much worse than this):

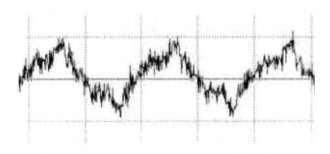

This distortion of the wave is caused by a number of things, including radio-frequency microwaves from DECT phones, Wi-Fi and other sources being picked up and carried around the building by the home wiring; plus electrical 'noise' or 'transients' from dimmer switches, fluorescent lighting, electronic transformers (such as your phone charger or laptop power supply) and appliances such as fridges, dishwashers, washing machines, hair dryers, vacuum cleaners and computers. Large facilities like hospital laboratories and manufacturers of electronics where there is sensitive equipment in use frequently have to install heavy-duty filtering devices on the incoming electricity supply to deal with this dirty electricity.

Anything that has a switched mode power supply (i.e. an electronic transformer) will create these transients - you can often see or hear it manifesting as interference on TVs and analogue radios when another device switches on or off. Dimmer switches and compact fluorescent lights are two of the worst offenders. Induction hobs, televisions and the AC inverters on solar panels are also common sources of DE. In domestic houses, the mains wiring can in some cases carry noise from external sources like a neighbouring commercial property. This is not common as domestic buildings should have a separate mains supply, but it's worth checking if you have a commercial premise next door. If you live in an apartment block you may also be picking up DE from neighbouring apartments that is propagating back along the common mains supply.

Some EHS sufferers seem to be particularly sensitive to dirty electricity in the home, and with the proliferation of electronic devices it is certainly a growing problem, so you may wish to check your wiring by hiring a DE meter and investing in some filters. Canadian researcher Dr

Magda Havas has conducted several studies involving sufferers with asthma, tinnitus, ADHD and even MS, which has symptoms very similar to EHS, whose symptoms improved dramatically once the electrical supply was cleaned up.[33]

Solutions

To clean the mains supply around the home, Dirty Electricity (DE) filter plugs are available that contain capacitors to 'soak up' the extraneous RF in the mains. Generally three or four of these will be sufficient for the entire house, but you will need to check with a DE meter frequently and experiment with the placing of the filter plugs to get the maximum benefit. You should concentrate on the areas where you spend the most time - for example around your bedroom, office desk, and living room. Filters need to be placed as close as possible to the source of the DE otherwise they can make the problem worse. You can hire DE meters and purchase filters from some of the suppliers listed at the end of the book.

Ferrite beads are inexpensive to buy and can be fitted to power leads, overhead light cables etc. to eliminate the surges and spikes and stop the cables re-radiating. Most sensitive electronic equipment will already have one of these fitted on the power lead to prevent equipment damage – these are the small cylindrical attachments that you often see on device cables, especially as electronic switched mode power supplies have largely replaced transformers on most devices these days. Ferrite beads are essentially a slug of iron that 'soaks up' any spikes and surges in the cable. Without these, many electronic gadgets like laptops or televisions would be unable to work properly.

To protect against irregular power surges and spikes in the supply, you should fit surge protectors to computers and sensitive equipment like your hi-fi. These are readily available in most electrical stores. More expensive versions will also include filters to prevent dirty electricity from the devices plugged into it from propagating back into the house mains. If your computer data is particularly valuable you may also wish to invest in an Uninterruptable Power Supply (UPS) that provides filtering and short-term power backup, usually from batteries or capacitors, in case of a power cut.

Note: If you are using dLAN or Powerline adaptors in place of Wi-Fi networks as I have earlier recommended, you should be aware that the signals generated by the adaptors should technically be classed as dirty electricity, although the levels are very low. You would be advised to switch these off when not in use.

Other Hazards

Desk lamps and Compact Fluorescent Lamps

Many low-voltage halogen and CFL desk lamps have transformers in the base. As with all similar electrical devices, your aim should be to keep the base unit containing the transformer as far from you as practical – at least 2 to 3 feet if you can.

Some unshielded compact fluorescent lamps (the ones that look like a coil or cluster of straight segments) have also been known to give off high levels of ultraviolet radiation that can cause skin damage. Don't sit close to these units unless they have an additional diffuser glass envelope, which will absorb the UV.

CFLs contain small amounts of toxic mercury and should not be carelessly disposed of with your regular trash. You can imagine the pollution of the water table resulting from an accumulation of mercury in landfill sites. Check to see if you can dispose of CFLs at your local Council recycling facility. Some areas may even *require* proper recycling of these lamps. If you suffer a breakage of a CFL lamp in the home, the US Environmental Protection Agency recommends first opening all windows and leaving the room to air for 5-10 minutes and then wearing gloves to pick up the pieces, using sticky tape to get all the small bits, before placing them into a glass jar or sealed plastic bag for disposal.[34]

Microwave ovens

Microwave ovens deserve a whole area of research in themselves for the detrimental effect they have on foodstuffs. These ovens produce free radicals in the food during cooking, which have been conclusively linked to an increased incidence in cancer. This is why you should leave food cooked in a microwave to stand for two or three minutes, to give the free radicals a chance to be re-absorbed into the food.

Leaving aside the detrimental effects on your food, microwaves contain heavy-duty transformers and give off high levels of power frequency EMFs at close range. The magnetic fields are often in excess of 2,000 nanoTesla at 1m range.

> Frequency range: 2.45GHz, the same as Wi-Fi and some mobile phones, with the difference that the radiation is not pulsed as it is not digitally encoded.

Microwave leakage around the door seal and through the glass door may be sufficient to cause problems in sensitive individuals. Try putting your mobile phone inside and then calling it to show that they are not 100% shielded. The current EU regulations require microwaves to have leakage of no more than $5mW/cm^2$ after a period of use, but many researchers consider even this level to be too high to be really safe. Check for leakage regularly – you can purchase rudimentary test meters for this purpose quite cheaply at many electronic or hardware stores.

If you really can't live without your microwave oven, at least ensure that you do not stand close to it when in use. Pregnant women, children and people with EHS should preferably leave the kitchen entirely when it is in use.

Wireless power charging (inductive charging)

Several manufacturers are promoting a system of inductive power charging for devices like phones, tablets and suchlike, and future developments include plans to power even moderately high-consumption devices like kitchen appliances wirelessly. The main standard is called Qi (pronounced "chee"), and essentially it depends on an inductive electromagnetic coupling between two coils, rather like a transformer. The primary coil is in the base station and the other is in the mobile device. When they are brought within a critical distance of each other, the primary coil induces a magnetic field in the secondary coil, located in the device, and electric current is generated. You will very likely already have some of these devices, for instance an electric cordless toothbrush with wall-mounted charging dock.

The original low-power Qi specification allowed for 5W of power to be transmitted, at a typical distance of 5mm; however it has been demonstrated that it is technically possible to send power up to 40mm at the moment, and this distance is likely to increase as the technology develops. Medium-power standards of up to 120W were introduced in 2011, and in 2015 a high-power standard of 1kW was demonstrated.

Qi charging pads are already being installed in several airport lounges and coffee shops, and IKEA has recently launched a range of Qi-enabled furniture. We can expect to see much more of this technology appearing in future.

Needless to say, the technology produces dangerously high power-frequency magnetic and electric fields around the primary base transformers. I certainly would not want to spend any length of time in the vicinity of a base station, so the idea of having one fitted in an armchair or desk, or even worse a bedside table, is completely abhorrent.

Other radio sources

Amateur radio transmitters, local taxi operators and the like can operate on various frequencies and being in close proximity to their aerials may trigger responses in sensitive individuals, so it is advisable to keep as much distance as possible from the masts or screen the wall that is closest to the mast.

Some military radar installations have equipment that may give off various forms of microwave radiation. There have been instances of this interfering with car locking systems in a similar way to TETRA transmitters. Most military communication frequencies are in the low VHF – UHF range, just above FM radio frequencies. These should not cause problems unless you live in close proximity to the transmitter where the power density will be high. The same applies to other radio and television transmitter masts.

Cars and other vehicles

Many newer cars can have surprisingly high levels of both low-frequency and microwave EMFs inside. The metal webbing used in radial tyres can become magnetised and can generate very low-frequency (VLF) pulsing EMFs as they rotate, which some EHS sufferers are affected by. The electrical power from batteries and other in-car electronics can also produce high magnetic fields. This is particularly problematic in electric and hybrid vehicles where the batteries may be located under the seats. The levels are very low compared with other magnetic field hazards, so unless you are extremely sensitive and make regular long journeys in your car it should not be too much of a problem, but extreme EHS sufferers may experience difficulty with some models. In tests, diesel cars produced the lowest EMFs, while electric and hybrid models had the highest readings.[35] Some relief if you are affected may be found by fitting an earthing pad or cushion on the driver's seat and grounding it to the car frame. For this to work effectively, you would also need to install a trailing anti-static grounding strip on the outside of the car; these are readily available at motor accessory stores.

Many new cars also come with Bluetooth and even Wi-Fi fitted as standard, which is something else to be aware of. Make sure you know how to disable these.

Airport body scanners

The new body scanners introduced in many airports that can image through clothing utilise terahertz radiation, mentioned in Chapter 1. Although terahertz radiation is widely believed to be completely safe due to its very low power and near-optical wavelength, it is a sad fact that there has been no long-term research conducted into the safety of these devices before their widespread introduction.

Terahertz waves are non-ionising and do not penetrate very far into the body due to its water content, making them *theoretically* less hazardous than microwaves, although much more research is needed here. One controversial 2010 report from Los Alamos scientist Boian Alexandrov claimed that terahertz radiation can cause genetic damage under high-intensity, long exposure resonant conditions, although the results were mixed and other researchers did not find this.[36] Some reports suggest that there may be subtle health effects similar to those caused by microwave frequencies, even though at present it appears that there is no conceivable mechanism for this. Largely as a result of these reports, there was much criticism over the hasty introduction of terahertz body scanners in airports, as they are essentially untested for safety; the lack of data means that there are as yet no scientifically-defined exposure levels for THz radiation.[37] However, the short exposure time in such scanners suggests that there is little cause for concern over occasional use.

Wind turbines

Another new and under-researched hazard, the turbines in wind farms have been reported by some people living in the vicinity to cause problems ranging from dizziness and nausea to depression, anxiety and even circulatory problems. The main issues seem to be general noise and infrasound when the turbines are active. Because of the irregular way the electricity is produced, wind turbines can also produce dirty electricity and excessive ground currents, also called stray voltage (see below).

Infrasound is the extremely low frequency sound (under 20Hz) below the threshold of human hearing. At even moderate levels this can be felt as a subtle vibration in various parts of the body, particularly the inner ear where the sensitive cilia can react to the vibration. Infrasound from turbines can also interact with the structure of a building, causing a subtle resonance inside it. Noise levels of course will vary depending on proximity and how active the turbines are, and I must emphasise that it is really a very small minority of people living in close proximity to turbines who seem affected by this. US researcher Dr Nina Pierpont has conducted surveys of people living within 2km of wind farms and identified a range of problems that they attributed to the turbines. Although Dr Pierpont's research has been heavily criticised as being methodologically flawed on several levels, her recommendation that no turbines be positioned closer to homes than 5km seems a reasonable precaution until more research has been done on their effects.[38]

Ground currents or stray voltage

Ground currents are a normal part of the way electricity is distributed, where a proportion of the current is returned to the substation through the ground. Under normal circumstances the ground currents are extremely low and nothing to be concerned about - in the order of 10 Volts or less - but in certain situations and atmospheric conditions it can be higher than this. There are a number of other ways in which stray voltage can be produced, usually involving corroded or faulty cabling that allows leakage into the surrounding earth; but the term 'stray voltage' tends to be generically applied to any situation where there is anomalous levels of current. It seems to be more of an issue in North America because of the design of their electrical distribution systems.

This current can sometimes be picked up by metal structures and pipes in the ground and the voltage may cause minor shocks when these are touched. It is more common in rural situations and dairy farmers in North America have long known about this as cows are frequently affected, displaying a variety of behavioural and health effects as well as reduced milk production.

However the problem is by no means limited to the countryside; a widely-reported case occurred in New York City in 2004 when a woman walking her dog was fatally electrocuted by ground current while standing on a metal plate. Many other instances of stray voltage in cities (usually involving dogs and lamp-posts) have been recorded, and electrical companies spend quite a bit of time dealing with stray voltages. In Direct Current

(DC) installations, such as those used in electric tram systems, the return current will tend to flow from the rails through the Earth back to the substation, taking the path of least resistance. If this involves flowing through any conductive pipes it can induce a voltage on the pipes, which may cause elevated levels of magnetic fields within your home or office if the pipes run immediately underneath the property. However, utility companies are more aware of the problems these days, and with proper modern earthing practices and increased use of plastic utility pipes, the issue of stray voltage is becoming less of a problem.

Conclusions

It seems that there is no stopping the rise of 'intelligent' microwave-based devices in our lives. Greater levels of environmental microwave exposure seem guaranteed. The 'internet of things' is upon us and the day is not too far off when everything in your home will have the capability to talk to the internet and each other. Recently I even read a proposal to equip farm animals with Wi-Fi transmitters, which would not only provide farmers with an easy tracking and locating tool, they could also link together as a mini smart grid to provide additional Wi-Fi coverage in rural areas!

With any new technology there is an inevitable period of adjustment, but in the case of pulsed microwave radiation, the technology is being introduced into our lives without undergoing any rigorous long-term testing procedures. As increasing numbers of people report symptoms that can be traced to exposure to these radiations, hopefully lower exposure guidelines will eventually be implemented in law, as many European countries are already doing. Until that happens, or until we evolve to better cope with the radiation levels, we can expect to see the rates of cancers and other ailments associated with EMF exposure continue to rise.

As we have seen, there are already moves in some European cities to ban or limit Wi-Fi in schools, and in France many public buildings like libraries are removing their Wi-Fi following an increase in staff illnesses. Meanwhile in the UK, the home improvement chain Homebase has recently issued all their floor staff with Bluetooth headsets that they have to wear all day. I wait with interest reports of increased sick leave from their staff.

Some enterprising communities where Wi-Fi and cell masts are banned have been set up in Europe specifically to provide electro-stress free environments for EHS sufferers. In the US, the area around the Green Bank radio telescope in West Virginia, a designated 'National Radio Quiet Zone' where wireless communications are strictly regulated to avoid interference with the telescope, attracts many EHS people to go and live there. As the technology and cell coverage proliferates, it is becoming increasingly difficult to find places where this is possible.

It is up to you to take the necessary precautions to reduce your exposure and protect yourself and your home, particularly your bedroom, from these radiations. It is not cheap or simple to completely screen a home without stripping it down to the bare walls and floors so this is best done as part of a major redevelopment, or installed as part of a new build. The easiest protection to implement is probably a bed canopy (with suitable screening underneath the bed of course) plus an earthing sheet on the bed; this will give you maximum protection during the night when your immune system needs the down-time to repair itself.

Armed with the knowledge in this booklet, you have the ability to continue to enjoy a certain level of technology, albeit in a controlled and responsible manner. I urge you to do your own research on the subject by investigating some of the links provided in the reference section at the end, and to take on the role of advocate for your friends and neighbours. By helping them reduce their own exposure you will be helping yourself as well.

Resources

Further research:

http://www.earthinginstitute.net/ - Information about sleeping earthed and the website of the book 'Earthing'.

http://www.emfs.info/ - Excellent and informative site from the UK National Grid about all aspects of power-frequency EMFs, including an overhead power line field calculator.

http://www.hese-project.org/ - International monitoring site.

http://www.ncbi.nlm.nih.gov/pmc/articles/PMC3265077/?tool= pubmed - Scientific study on the benefits of sleeping earthed.

http://www.powerwatch.org.uk/ - For the most up-to-date scientific research on all technopathic stress issues.

https://www.rfsafe.com/ - Very informative US site, has SAR ratings on all leading phones, sells 'RF Safety kits'.

http://royriggs.co.uk/ - Roy is a dowser and geobiologist, his site has lots of good information about technostress.

http://stopsmartmeters.org.uk/ - Essential site for up-to date information and campaigning aids on 'smart meters'.

http://stopsmartmeters.org/ - US version of the above site.

http://www.tetrawatch.net/ - Researching and campaigning against TETRA (Airwave).

http://www.wifiinschools.com/ - Another site about children's exposure to Wi-Fi, with good scientific data.

http://wiredchild.org/ - Well-constructed site for parents concerned about their children's exposure to EMFs.

UK suppliers:

http://www.abacaorganic.co.uk/ - Suppliers of organic natural latex mattresses.

http://www.devolo.com/uk/ - Powerline dLAN adaptors.

http://emfclothing.com/ – protective clothing and shielding materials.

http://www.emfields-solutions.com/ - Sells everything you need; screening materials, air tube headsets, test meters, dirty electricity filters, bed canopies etc., and you can buy or hire measuring equipment.

http://www.gigaset.com/ – low-radiation DECT cordless phones.

http://www.netgear.com/ – Powerline dLAN adaptors and routers.

http://www.stetzer.co.uk/ - UK distributors of 'Stetzerizer' dirty electricity filters, earthing sheets, absorbent wallpaper and air tube headsets.

US/Canada suppliers:

http://www.devolo.com/ - Powerline dLAN adaptors.

http://www.emfields-solutions.com/other/agents.asp - Overseas suppliers for EMFields products.

http://www.getpurepower.ca/ - Canadian supplier of 'Stetzerizer' dirty electricity filters and meters.

http://www.lessemf.com/ - Screening materials, clothing, test equipment.

http://www.magneticsciences.com/ - Suppliers of test meters and equipment.

http://www.netgear.com/ – Powerline dLAN adaptors and routers.

https://www.rfsafe.com/ - US site dedicated to phone safety, sells air-tube headsets, shielding materials, clothing etc.

http://www.slt.co/ - Meters, shielding materials etc.

http://www.stetzerizer-us.com/ - Meters of all sorts and filters for dirty electricity, air-tube headsets.

Books:

Dirty Electricity, Samuel Milham, MD, MPH, Rising Star 2010

Earthing, Clinton Ober, Stephen T. Sinatra MD, Martin Zucker, Basic Health Publications, 2010

EMF and Microwave Protection for you and your family, Alasdair & Jean Philips, Powerwatch 2003

The Invisible Disease, Gunni Nordström, O books 2004

The Powerwatch Handbook, Alasdair & Jean Philips, Piatkus, 2006

Safe as Houses? David Cowan & Rodney Girdlestone, 1996

Water, Electricity and Health, Alan Hall, Hawthorn, 1998

Zapped, Ann Louse Gittleman, Harper One 2010

Find this information on the web:
http://geomancygroup.org/secular-space/technopathic-stress/

All links were correct at time of printing.

References

[1] http://www.emfields-solutions.com/faq.asp#wlans

[2] http://stopsmartmeters.org.uk/wifi-banned-in-pre-school-childcare-facilities-by-french-government-2/

[3] http://stopsmartmeters.org.uk/lloyds-of-london-excludes-liability-coverage-for-harm-from-wireless-radiationrf-emf/

[4] http://www.iarc.fr/en/media-centre/pr/2011/pdfs/pr208_E.pdf

[5] http://stopsmartmeters.org.uk/former-nokia-chief-mobile-phones-wrecked-my-health/

[6] 'Ionising' means that the radiation has enough energy to remove electrons from an atom that it interacts with, causing the atom to become charged or ionised.

[7] http://www.ibtimes.co.uk/lifi-internet-breakthrough-224gbps-connection-broadcast-led-bulb-1488204

[8] http://en.wikipedia.org/wiki/Microwave_oven

[9] http://www.dailymail.co.uk/sciencetech/article-1287842/As-scientists-warn-regular-mobile-use-CAN-cause-cancer-just-safe-mobile-phone.html

[10] http://www.bioinitiative.org/report/wp-content/uploads/pdfs/sec20_2012_Findings_in_Autism_Consistent_with_EMF_and_RFR.pdf

[11] Information sheet #13 from http://www.es-uk.info/

[12] http://www.powerwatch.org.uk/news/2015-03-08-lerchl-RF-co-carcinogen.asp

[13] https://www.youtube.com/watch?v=018C2oG2Rcs

[14] McCarty DE, Carrubba S, Chesson AL, et al. Electromagnetic hypersensitivity: Evidence for a novel neurological syndrome. Int. J. Neurosci. 2011; 121(12): 670-676

[15] http://www.pathophysiologyjournal.com/article/S0928-4680%2814%2900064-9/abstract

[16] http://en.wikipedia.org/wiki/Wi-Fi

[17] http://www.thestar.com/news/queenspark/2015/01/22/thousands-of-smart-meters-in-ontario-to-be-removed-over-safety-worries.html

18

http://www.theregister.co.uk/2013/07/19/feature_uk_gov_pow
er_meter_plan/
[19] http://smartgridawareness.org/2015/10/29/smart-meters-
have-life-of-5-to-7-years/
[20] http://stopsmartmeters.org.uk/new-report-warns-of-smart-
meter-failures-due-to-temperature-weather-extremes/
[21] http://gizmodo.com/las-new-streetlamps-will-keep-cell-
service-running-afte-1741056846
[22] http://www.theregister.co.uk/2012/02/01/smart_meters_yesno/
[23] http://www.electricsense.com/1010/bluetooth-what-you-will-
learn-nowhere-else-%E2%80%93-is-it-really-dangerous/
[24] http://www.biogeometry.ca/#!the-miracle-of-hemberg/cu3q
[25] https://nakedsecurity.sophos.com/2015/09/15/smartwatch-
sensors-can-be-used-to-eavesdrop-on-the-keys-youre-typing/
[26] http://www.renalandurologynews.com/cell-phone-use-
could-damage-semen/article/157370/
[27] http://www.newscientist.com/article/dn7460-large-study-
links-power-lines-to-childhood-cancer.html
28

http://www.nature.com/index.html?file=/bjc/journal/v88/n12/ful
l/6601010a.html
[29] Mainly Singapore, Indonesia, UAE and parts of Ireland.
[30] http://www.bbc.co.uk/news/technology-31296188
[31] US Patent no. 20120304206 "Methods and Systems for
Presenting an Advertisement Associated with an Ambient
Action of a User."
[32] http://www.huffingtonpost.com/dr-douglas-fields/left-sided-
cancer--should_b_629572.html
[33] http://www.magdahavas.com/multiple-sclerosis-and-dirty-
electricity/
[34] http://www2.epa.gov/cfl/cleaning-broken-cfl
[35] http://www.saferemr.com/2014/07/shouldnt-hybrid-and-
electric-cars-be-re.html
[36] http://www.technologyreview.com/view/416066/how-
terahertz-waves-tear-apart-dna/
[37] https://www.rp-photonics.com/terahertz_radiation.html
[38] http://stopthesethings.com/2014/07/05/nina-pierpont-
warns-against-an-entirely-avoidable-turkish-wind-farm-
disaster/

Index

About the Author

One of the most respected dowsers in the UK and internationally, Grahame is a professional dowser and geomancer specialising in geopathic and technopathic remedial work, and consulting on the creation of sacred spaces such as stone circles and labyrinths.

Grahame is a professional member and registered tutor of The British Society of Dowsers and served as President of the Society from 2008-2014. He has written numerous articles for the society's journal 'Dowsing Today', produces an award-winning podcast 'Adventures in Dowsing', and in 2014 was awarded the BSD Award for exceptional services to dowsing and the society. He is also a member of the Canadian and American dowsing societies, a founder member of The Geomancy Group and co-chair of International Dowsers, created with Susan Collins of Canada to foster greater links between European and North American dowsing communities.

Grahame has been a guest speaker and workshop leader at conferences of the Canadian Questers, Canadian Society of Dowsers, Escola Nacional de Feng-Shui in Lisbon, the Japanese Dowsing Society, and several times at the American Society of Dowsers. In 2014 he was gifted his native name 'Carrier of the Sacred Fire' by First Nations Elder White Eagle at the ASD convention. He and Elspeth live in Glasgow, Scotland.

His previous book 'Dowsing Magic' is published by Penwith Press.

You can contact Grahame through his website at http://westerngeomancy.org/